C000281529

how to...

write the
ECC Works Information

For use with the Engineering and Construction Contract

An NEC document

April 2013

Construction Clients' Board endorsement of NEC3

The Construction Clients' Board recommends that public sector organisations use the NEC3 contracts when procuring construction. Standardising use of this comprehensive suite of contracts should help to deliver efficiencies across the public sector and promote behaviours in line with the principles of *Achieving Excellence in Construction*.

Cabinet Office UK

neccontract.com

NEC is a division of Thomas Telford Ltd, which is a wholly owned subsidiary of the Institution of Civil Engineers (ICE), the owner and developer of the NEC.

The NEC is a family of standard contracts, each of which has these characteristics:

- Its use stimulates good management of the relationship between the two parties to the contract and, hence, of the work included in the contract.

- It can be used in a wide variety of commercial situations, for a wide variety of types of work and in any location.

- It is a clear and simple document – using language and a structure which are straightforward and easily understood.

NEC3 how to write the ECC Works Information is one of the NEC family and is consistent with all other NEC3 documents.

ISBN (complete box set) 978 0 7277 5867 5
ISBN (this document) 978 0 7277 5907 8
ISBN Engineering and Construction Contract) 978 0 7277 5865 1
ISBN (Engineering and Construction Contract Guidance Notes) 978 0 7277 5903 0
ISBN (Engineering and Construction Contract Flow Charts) 978 0 7277 5905 4
ISBN (how to use the ECC communication forms) 978 0 7277 5909 2

Reprinted (thrice) 2015
Reprinted with amendments 2015

British Library Cataloguing in Publication Data for this publication is available from the British Library.

Typeset by Academic + Technical, Bristol

Printed and bound in Great Britain by Bell & Bain Limited, Glasgow, UK

CONTENTS

FOREWORD

I was delighted to be asked to write the Foreword for the NEC3 Contracts.

I have followed the outstanding rise and success of NEC contracts for a number of years now, in particular during my tenure as the 146th President of the Institution of Civil Engineers, 2010/11.

In my position as UK Government's Chief Construction Adviser, I am working with Government and industry to ensure Britain's construction sector is equipped with the knowledge, skills and best practice it needs in its transition to a low carbon economy. I am promoting innovation in the sector, including in particular the use of Building Information Modelling (BIM) in public sector construction procurement; and the synergy and fit with the collaborative nature of NEC contracts is obvious. The Government's construction strategy is a very significant investment and NEC contracts will play an important role in setting high standards of contract preparation, management and the desirable behaviour of our industry.

In the UK, we are faced with having to deliver a 15–20 per cent reduction in the cost to the public sector of construction during the lifetime of this Parliament. Shifting mind-set, attitude and behaviour into best practice NEC processes will go a considerable way to achieving this.

Of course, NEC contracts are used successfully around the world in both public and private sector projects; this trend seems set to continue at an increasing pace. NEC contracts are, according to my good friend and NEC's creator Dr Martin Barnes CBE, about better management of projects. This is quite achievable and I encourage you to understand NEC contracts to the best you can and exploit the potential this offers us all.

Peter Hansford

UK Government's Chief Construction Adviser
Cabinet Office

PREFACE

The NEC contracts are the only suite of standard contracts designed to facilitate and encourage good management of the projects on which they are used. The experience of using NEC contracts around the world is that they really make a difference. Previously, standard contracts were written mainly as legal documents best left in the desk drawer until costly and delaying problems had occurred and there were lengthy arguments about who was to blame.

The language of NEC contracts is clear and simple, and the procedures set out are all designed to stimulate good management. Foresighted collaboration between all the contributors to the project is the aim. The contracts set out how the interfaces between all the organisations involved will be managed – from the client through the designers and main contractors to all the many subcontractors and suppliers.

Versions of the NEC contract are specific to the work of professional service providers such as project managers and designers, to main contractors, to subcontractors and to suppliers. The wide range of situations covered by the contracts means that they do not need to be altered to suit any particular situation.

The NEC contracts are the first to deal specifically and effectively with management of the inevitable risks and uncertainties which are encountered to some extent on all projects. Management of the expected is easy, effective management of the unexpected draws fully on the collaborative approach inherent in the NEC contracts.

Most people working on projects using the NEC contracts for the first time are hugely impressed by the difference between the confrontational characteristics of traditional contracts and the teamwork engendered by the NEC. The NEC does not include specific provisions for dispute avoidance. They are not necessary. Collaborative management itself is designed to avoid disputes and it really works.

It is common for the final account for the work on a project to be settled at the time when the work is finished. The traditional long period of expensive professional work after completion to settle final payments just is not needed.

The NEC contracts are truly a massive change for the better for the industries in which they are used.

Dr Martin Barnes CBE

Originator of the NEC contracts

ACKNOWLEDGEMENTS

The original NEC was designed and drafted by Dr Martin Barnes then of Coopers and Lybrand with the assistance of Professor J. G. Perry then of the University of Birmingham, T.W. Weddell then of Travers Morgan Management, T.H. Nicholson, Consultant to the Institution of Civil Engineers, A Norman then of the University of Manchester Institute of Science and Technology and P.A. Baird then Corporate Contracts Consultant, Eskom, South Africa.

NEC wishes to acknowledge and thank the *how to write the ECC Works Information* project team for their input to this guidance.

Members of the project team include: M. Garratt, I. Griffiths, P. Higgins, T. Knee-Robinson, N. C. Shaw.

The members of the NEC Panel are:

    N. C. Shaw, FCIPS, CEng, MIMechE (Chairman)
    F. Alderson, BA (Melb), Solicitor
    P. A. Baird, BSc, CEng, FICE, M(SA)ICE, MAPM
    M. Codling, BSc, ICIOB, MAPM
    L. T. Eames, BSc, FRICS, FCIOB
    M. Garratt, BSc(Hons), MRICS, FCIArb
    J. J. Lofty, MRICS

NEC Consultant:

    R. A. Gerrard BSc(Hons), FRICS, FCIArb, FCInstCES

Chapter 1 Introduction

The purpose of this guide is to help users to produce Works Information for the NEC3 Engineering and Construction Contract (ECC).

The convention of using italics for terms which are identified in the Contract Data of the ECC and capital initials for terms defined in the ECC has been used in this guide.

Good quality Works Information is vital to achieving better outcomes for projects and reducing misunderstandings and disputes. Works Information should be prepared with individual project requirements and the operation of the ECC in mind.

All NEC contracts refer to 'information' which sets out what the Parties are required to do under the contract. The obligation to work in accordance with that information is set out in the *conditions of contract*.

The diagram below shows the relationship between the constituent parts of a contract including the Works Information. Contract Data identifies the documents forming the contract. The *conditions of contract* refer to each part of the contract and require information to be stated in them. The form of agreement may be used to record the agreement between the Parties on the basis of the Contract Data, or the Parties may rely on an exchange of correspondence to establish the contract.

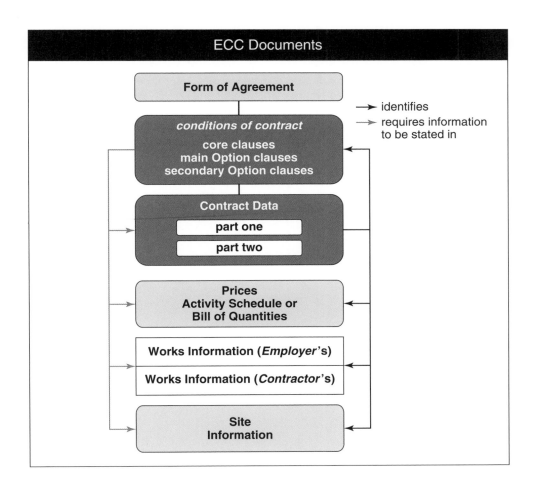

Information and documents required for the contract must be in the right part of the contract. If documents are located in the wrong place, it may cause confusion and risk that the documents are not properly incorporated. For example, information which describes the *works* must be identified in the Works Information. The diagram shows that Works Information is identified in Contract Data. Therefore, all documents and information which describe the *works* or state constraints must be identified as Works Information and listed in Contract Data. This includes information contained within correspondence and minutes of meetings which describes the *works* to be provided. The approach which results in the least uncertainty is to extract relevant information from correspondence and minutes of meetings and properly integrate it in the Works Information. Works Information will often consist of multiple documents and sections, in which case a contents list should be provided.

The clarity achieved by this contract structure and the separation of its parts is helpful to users and significantly reduces ambiguity and the potential for disputes.

This guidance will help users to draft and assemble Works Information correctly. Chapter 2 describes the status of Works Information and the relationship between Works Information and the other parts of the ECC. Chapter 3 provides advice on drafting and how to achieve clarity. Chapter 4 is a checklist of information to be provided in Works Information, as required by the *conditions of contract*. Chapter 5 suggests an outline structure, including a list of topics to be considered for inclusion in the Works Information.

The requirement for good 'information' describing the work or services to be provided applies to all contracting systems. It is an objective of NEC to provide a contract which is clear and simple and promotes effective management and delivery of the *works*.

Chapter 2 The status of Works Information

The function of Works Information

Works Information is defined as

> **"11.2(19) Works Information is information which either**
>
> - **specifies and describes the *works* or**
> - **states any constraint on how the *Contractor* Provides the Works**
>
> **and is either**
>
> - **in the documents which the Contract Data states it is in or**
> - **in an instruction given in accordance with this contract."**

Works Information should be a complete and precise statement of the *Employer*'s requirements. If it is not, there is a risk that the *Contactor* will interpret it differently from the *Employer*'s intention.

Works Information prepared by the *Employer* is separated from Works Information prepared by the *Contractor* relating to his design. The *Employer*'s Works Information is prepared first and the *Contractor* uses this to prepare the information relating to his design. The *Employer*'s Works Information has priority over the *Contractor*'s Works Information under ECC clause 60.1(1).

Works Information provided by the *Employer* includes

- technical information, specifications and drawings describing the *works,*
- constraints on how the *Contractor* Provides the Works, including specific safety requirements and
- *Employer*'s requirements for work to be designed by the *Contractor*.

Works Information provided by the *Contractor* is particulars of the *Contractor*'s design for *works* he is required to design.

The *Contractor*'s primary obligation under ECC is stated in clause 20.1.

> **"20.1 The *Contractor* Provides the Works in accordance with the Works Information."**

When this clause is read in conjunction with clause 11.2(19) and the following clauses, the importance of Works Information is clear.

> **"11.2(2) Completion is when the *Contractor* has**
>
> - **done all the work which the Works Information states he is to do by the Completion Date and . . . ."**

> **"11.2(5) A Defect is**
>
> - **a part of the *works* which is not in accordance with the Works Information or . . . . . ."**

> **"60.1 The following are compensation events.**
>
> **(1) The *Project Manager* gives an instruction changing the Works Information except**
>
> - **a change made in order to correct a Defect or**
> - **a change to the Works Information provided by the *Contractor* for his design which is made either at his request or to comply with other Works Information provided by the *Employer*."**

The *conditions of contract* make frequent reference to Works Information as illustrated above and later in Chapter 4. Works Information is therefore central to the operation of the contract.

Works Information should be drafted in accordance with the three key objectives of NEC, namely flexibility, clarity and stimulus to good management.

The relationship between Works Information and Contract Data

Contract Data contains information needed to operate the contract, including the choice of main and secondary Options. Contract Data is the type of information often described in other forms of contract as the contract particulars or appendix. There are two parts. Part one contains the information provided by the *Employer* and part two is where the *Contractor*'s data and proposals are identified.

The ECC Guidance Notes contain detailed information on completion of the Contract Data.

The information set out in the Contract Data is not Works Information or Site Information, but it identifies the documents which contain Works Information. The *Employer* identifies the documents which contain his Works Information in Contract Data part one. The *Contractor* identifies the documents which contain the Works Information for his design in Contract Data part two. Where information is in non-documentary form such as models, they should be identified and their availability and location stated.

Works Information should not contain information which repeats, contradicts or creates an ambiguity with any information contained within Contract Data or with the *conditions of contract*.

The following documents are identified within Contract Data and are not Works Information

- *boundaries of the site,*
- Partnering Information (if Option X12 is used),
- *incentive schedule* (if Option X20 is used),
- matters to be included in the initial Risk Register,
- information describing the Working Areas and
- the programme (if required at tender stage).

A further distinction is that the *Project Manager* can instruct a change to Works Information but cannot change Contract Data once the contract is formed.

The relationship between Works Information and Site Information

The *Contractor*'s obligations regarding Works Information and Site Information are different. A clear separation between Works and Site Information is required. Site Information describes the condition of the Site before work starts. Works Information describes what is to be done on the Site.

Site Information is defined as follows

> **"11.2(16) Site Information is information which**
>
> - **describes the Site and its surroundings and**
> - **is in the documents which the Contract Data states it is in."**

Site is defined as

> **"11.2(15) The Site is the area within the *boundaries of the site* and the volumes above and below it which are affected by work included in this contract."**

Site Information, as with Works Information, is incorporated by reference to documents listed in Contract Data. There are several distinctions between Site Information and Works Information, for example

- Site Information cannot be changed once the contract is formed.
- Site Information is used to assess compensation events resulting from physical conditions (clauses 60.1(12) and 60.2).
- Ambiguities or inconsistencies in the Site Information are resolved in favour of the *Contractor* (clause 60.3). This encourages full disclosure of information on the condition of the Site.

Site Information may include the following

- Subsoil investigation borehole records and test results.
- Reports obtained by the *Employer* concerning the physical conditions of the Site or its surroundings. This may include mapping, hydrographic data and hydrological information.
- References to publicly available information about the Site and surroundings, such as published papers and interpretations of the geological survey.
- Information about pipes, services and other objects below the surface of the Site.
- Information about buildings, structures and other features (including machinery adjacent to and on the Site).

Site Information is provided to help the *Contractor* to prepare his tender, to decide his method of working and programme and prepare designs for which he is responsible. Only factual information about the physical condition of the Site and its surroundings is included in Site Information. Statements of opinion – for example interpretation of soil investigation surveys – are not Site Information.

Some documents may contain both Works Information and Site Information. For example, a document may show an existing structure alongside details of a new structure. The following example shows how Site Information and Works Information can be separated.

Works Information – Example Drawing List

Drawing No.	Description
0100	New Factory Building
0200	Existing Factory Building (proposed features)

Site Information – Example Drawing List

Drawing No.	Description
0200	Existing Factory Building (existing features)
0300	Existing Mains Services

The relationship between Works Information and pricing documents

A clear distinction exists between Works Information and the pricing documents i.e. the Activity Schedule or Bill of Quantities. Information in the pricing documents explains the Prices and should not describe the *works*. The *Contractor*'s obligation is to Provide the Works in accordance with the Works Information.

Statements about pricing of work should not be in the Works Information, as they neither specify or describe the *works*, nor do they state constraints.

Information in the pricing documents does not change the obligation of the *Contractor* to Provide the Works in accordance with the Works Information.

Works Information as a contract document

Some forms of contract use provisions creating a hierarchy or priority of documentation as a means of resolving ambiguities and inconsistencies in or between documents. This is not the approach taken by NEC.

Priority clauses can interfere with the natural interpretation of documents as intended by the Parties. Such an indiscriminate approach to resolving ambiguities and inconsistencies can cause problems.

As explained in Chapter 1, the ECC describes the function of each document forming part of the contract. This provides clarity as to the relevance and purpose of each document in the contract. The *conditions of contract* then deal with any remaining ambiguity or inconsistency in or between the documents.

The ECC deals with ambiguities and inconsistencies between the documents forming the contract at clause 17.1.

> **"The *Project Manager* or the *Contractor* notifies the other as soon as either becomes aware of an ambiguity or inconsistency in or between the documents which are part of this contract. The *Project Manager* gives an instruction resolving the ambiguity or inconsistency."**

Such an instruction from the *Project Manager* changing the Works Information is a compensation event (clause 60.1(1), second bullet) except where the instruction is a

> **"change to the Works Information provided by the *Contractor* for his design which is made either at his request or to comply with other Works Information provided by the *Employer*."**

There is no priority of documents in ECC other than the hierarchy of *Employer*'s Works Information compared to *Contractor*'s Works Information in clause 60.1(1). Works Information should be drafted to avoid any conflicts or contradictions. Works Information may consist of several documents drafted by different contributors. Ambiguities or inconsistencies between documents should be corrected before the documents are issued.

Chapter 3 Drafting Works Information

Incorporation of standard specifications

Works Information should be clear, complete and precise. Subjective terms should be avoided to reduce the risk of misinterpretation and dispute.

Standard specifications drafted for use on previous projects or with other standard forms of contract should be reviewed and amended as appropriate, prior to incorporation. Drafting shortcuts such as 'All references to Specification shall mean Works Information' is likely to cause problems. Each reference should be checked for correct use in relation to the duties and responsibilities of the *Employer*, *Contractor*, *Project Manager* and *Supervisor*.

The duties of the *Project Manager* and the *Supervisor* are set out in the *conditions of contract*.

The substitution of '*Project Manager*' for 'Engineer' as a drafting short-cut can cause confusion for the following reasons.

- The ECC *Project Manager* may not have the same duties as the Engineer in other contracts. Some of the Engineer's duties may be undertaken by the *Project Manager* and some by the *Supervisor* or *Adjudicator*.
- The ECC is more prescriptive on what can be done by the *Project Manager* on certification than other standard contracts.
- The 'acceptance' of a communication by a *Project Manager* may differ from an 'approval' given by an Engineer in other contracts. ECC clause 14.1 states

"The *Project Manager*'s or the *Supervisor*'s acceptance of a communication from the *Contractor* or of his work does not change the *Contractor*'s responsibility to Provide the Works or his liability for his design."

Standard specifications should be checked to ensure consistency with other parts of the contract. For example, risk allocation varies from contract to contract and references to *Employer*'s and *Contractor*'s responsibilities within standard specifications need to be checked.

In their publication *Managing Reality* (Thomas Telford Publishing, 2012), Mitchell and Trebes give the following examples of specification ambiguity.

Examination of typical traditional specification

W.1	Water mains
W1.1	If, in the opinion of the Engineer, there is undue delay in the application of the first hydraulic test, or of any subsequent tests, or if any length of main should fail the test, the Engineer may direct the Contractor to suspend main laying operations until the length or lengths of main have been satisfactorily tested.
	[Note subjective words, 'in the opinion of' and 'satisfactorily', as well as the uncertainty regarding the Engineer's actions and the use of the term Engineer.]

W1.2	After satisfactory completion of pressure testing, each valve on and adjacent to, the pipeline shall be examined to witness that the opening/closing mechanisms function satisfactorily and are capable of functioning for their designated purpose. Isolating valves shall be examined by opening and closing the isolating gate three times. All tests and examinations shall be witnessed by the Engineer's staff and the Contractor shall provide a witnessed certificate to this effect to the Engineer.
	[Note subjective word 'satisfactorily' and the use of the wrong terminology. The witnessing of the tests should be by the *Supervisor*. If a preface had been included in this specification to the effect that read *Project Manager* for Engineer, then the *Project Manager* would have an obligation that is the *Supervisor*'s under the *conditions of contract* and a conflict would exist. Note also that the *Contractor* is required to provide notification of results under the *conditions of contract* and this Works Information paragraph requires an extra obligation of the *Contractor*.]
W2	**Swabbing of water mains**
W2.1	*Swabs will be provided by the Purchaser.* Temporary pipework shall be provided by the Contractor.
	[Note wrong terminology in Purchaser, where it should refer to *Employer*. Note also the vague nature of the statement. How many swabs will be provided? Where will/can they be obtained from?]
W3	**Water supply for testing and swabbing**
W3.1	For the purpose of the hydraulic testing of water-retaining structures and pipelines, the Purchaser will make available water from existing mains, at times and rates of flow to be decided by the Purchaser and agreed with the Engineer.
	[Note wrong terminology: should be *Project Manager* and *Employer*, not Purchaser and Engineer. Note also that if the *Contractor* were to do the test, he is not involved in the decision of when the water is to be provided, although this could affect his programme.]
W3.2	Water will be provided free of charge to the Contractor for the first test. In the event of any part of the work having to be retested the Contractor shall be required to pay for the supply of water on a volume basis at the prevailing rate of the Purchaser.
	[Note wrong terminology: should be *Employer*, not Purchaser.]
G1	**Standards of materials**
G1.1	15th Statement of the DoE Committee on Chemicals and Materials of Constructions for use in Public Water Supplies and Swimming Pools.
G1.2	The use of materials, including chemicals that do not meet the above criteria, shall be subject to the approval of the Engineer.
	[Note under the *conditions of contract* 'acceptance' and not 'approval' is the terminology used. Also should be the *Project Manager*, not Engineer.]

G2	Disinfection of pipework and structures
	Pipes, pumps and structures shall be disinfected in accordance with the following procedure:
(a)	The Contractor shall provide, at least three weeks before carrying out the disinfection process, a <u>Method Statement</u> to the <u>Engineer</u> for his <u>Approval</u>.
	[Note that under the *conditions of contract* a method statement is part of the *Contractor*'s programme. The *Contractor* submits his programme to the *Project Manager* (not the Engineer) for acceptance (not approval). There are several programme revisions provided for in the *conditions of contract*, including where the *Project Manager* can ask for one at any time.]
(b)	After <u>satisfactory</u> hydraulic testing, pipes, pumps, structures etc shall be cleaned of all deleterious material.
	[Note the use of vague words such as 'satisfactory'. The expected results of the test, as well as the details of how and when the test is to be carried out, should be provided.]
(c)	The volume to be disinfected shall be filled with chlorinated water at a dose level of 20–25 mg/l free chlorine and left to stand for 24 hours. Large structures may have all surfaces thoroughly scrubbed down with heavily chlorinated water and the volume then filled with a lower dose level, 0.5 mg/l chlorinated water and left for 24 hours.
(d)	The chlorinated water shall be drained away and disposed of in a <u>safe</u> and <u>satisfactory</u> manner. All <u>necessary</u> approvals for discharge shall be obtained by the Contractor. De-chlorination will be necessary to ensure that free chlorine discharged is below 0.1 mg/l, where discharge is a watercourse, or drain leading to a watercourse.
	[Note the vague words 'safe', 'satisfactory' and 'necessary'. What is safe and satisfactory to the *Contractor* could be different from the *Project Manager*. Unless a published standard is quoted, the requirements should be stated in the Works Information.]
(e)	The volume shall then be refilled with potable water and left a further 24 hours.
(f)	<u>The Purchaser will take samples for bacteriological testing</u>. The results of his test will take a minimum of three working days to provide a conclusive test.
	[Note the incorrect terminology by the use of 'Purchaser' rather than *Employer*. The Works Information is required to state who provides samples, materials and facilities for testing. The criteria of the test should also be stated.]
(g)	<u>If test results are unsatisfactory to the Purchaser, the above procedure shall be repeated until satisfactory results are achieved.</u>
	[Note: use of incorrect terminology 'Purchaser' and 'satisfactory'. The uncertainty of this statement could leave the *Contractor* having difficulties pricing accurately, or potentially adding conservative amounts of risk into his price.]

Health and safety information

Clause 27.4 requires the *Contractor* to act in accordance with the health and safety requirements stated in the Works Information. Further comment on this clause is given in Chapters 4 and 5.

Employers should consider how to deal with health and safety requirements and documentation carefully when preparing Works Information. The associated constraints on how the *Contractor* Provides the Works should be included in the *Employer*'s Works Information.

Many jurisdictions require health and safety risks to be evaluated by the *Employer* and then communicated to the *Contractor* as part of the procurement process. It may not be necessary to include the risk evaluation as a contract document, but it is necessary to check for consistency between the health and safety information, Works Information and Site Information.

UK Specific illustration:

The Construction (Design and Management) Regulations 2007 requires the preparation of Pre-Construction Information relating to health and safety and for this information to be provided to the *Contractor*. This may contain information which is both Works Information and Site Information. Care should be taken in deciding whether and how to include the Pre-Construction Information in the contract. Consider

- whether the information is Works Information or Site Information (see Chapter 2),
- how changes and developments to the information will be administered which changes can only be made by an instruction of the *Project Manager* and which can be changed by the *Contractor* to suit his own proposals,
- the legal requirement for Pre-Construction Information to be issued to the *Contractor* and
- the time difference between formation of the contract and the *starting date* – during which the Pre-Construction Information may change.

In most cases, clarity will be achieved by keeping the Pre-Construction Information as a separate document. However, the Works Information must include information from the Pre-Construction Information which describes the *works* or states constraints and the Site Information must include or identify information which describes the Site.

General drafting advice

The following description of NEC drafting style will help users draft Works Information and other contract documents clearly.

1. A basic objective of NEC contracts is that they should be clear and simple. The drafting delivers clarity and simplicity of language. Simplicity also follows from the design of the management processes in the contracts.

2. One of the objects of using simple language in the contracts is that they should be easy for people whose first language is not English to use. A further advantage is that the contracts can be translated into other languages accurately.

Vocabulary

3. Use the simplest possible words. Simple words have few syllables.

4. Do not use words which are not needed.

Sentences

5. Sentences should be as short as possible. Twenty words is fine. Never have more than forty. Use several short sentences instead of one sentence with several clauses.

6. Many statements are conditional. 'If this happens, the *Contractor* does this'. Put the condition first, not last and use 'if', not 'when'. 'If this happens, the *Contractor* does this.' [not: 'The *Contractor* does this when this happens.'] Use 'when' only if timing is implied as in clause 36.3.

7. Use commas properly. The pause which a comma creates can help understanding.

Bullets

8. Bullets are used when a clause includes a list. Do not use bullets for short lists with short descriptions. The following does not need to be bulleted:

    ''The *Contractor* arranges for 'Hail to the Chief' to be played by a brass band outside the *Project Manager*'s office at 9 a.m. on

    *   Mondays,
    *   Wednesdays,
    *   Fridays and
    *   his birthday.''

9. A useful check is that punctuation of bulleted sentences should work if the bullets are removed. Bullets end with a comma except the last but one which ends with 'and' or 'or' and the last which ends with a full stop. Do not put a comma before 'and'. 'And' replaces the comma before the last item on a list as above.

10. Whenever possible, put bullets at the end of a sentence. Having a bit more of the sentence after a bulleted list is clumsy as the reader does not expect the text and the sentence can become very long and not easy to understand.

11. Bullets are indented. Bullets within bullets should be avoided if possible. If used, as in clause 31.2, use a double indent.

Adjectives and Adverbs

12. Old-fashioned contracts use a lot of adjectives and adverbs. NEC contracts use the absolute minimum, which is hardly any. This is perhaps the most important drafting convention for NEC. Use an adverb or adjective only if it is really unavoidable.

13. Verbs and nouns are usually precise, adverbs and adjectives are usually imprecise. 'The *Contractor* does all urgent work quickly' is easy to understand. Unfortunately, you can argue about the meaning of 'urgent' (adjective) and 'quickly' (adverb). 'The *Contractor*' (noun), 'does' (verb) and 'work' (noun) are precise. To make the point absurdly, 'George ate a hefty meal unhurriedly' is vague but not meaningless. 'George ate a meal of 42 mouthfuls in 21 minutes' is boring but precise. Contracts are not intended to be a good read. They have to state who does what in words of unarguable precision and clarity.

14. Some adverbial phrases are as imprecise as adverbs, e.g. 'quickly' in 'come quickly' is obviously an adverb. So, in effect, is 'as soon as you can' in 'come as soon as you can'.

15. This text, for example, about extension of time, comes from clause 44(1) of the ICE conditions fifth edition, adverbs and adjectives in italics.

© nec 2013 | neccontract.com   how to write the ECC Works Information   11

'................. or *exceptional adverse* weather conditions or other *special* circumstances of any kind .... be such as *fairly* to entitle the Contractor to an extension of time .... the Contractor shall within 28 days after the cause of the delay has arisen or as *soon thereafter* as is *reasonable* in all the circumstances deliver to the engineer *full* and *detailed* particulars of any claim to extension of time ....'

16. It is impossible to decide whether an extension of time should be given and, if so, for how much, when and how described until the courts have decided what the adjectives and adverbs mean.

17. NEC drafting requires the absolute minimum of adverbs and adjectives. Some are innocuous as in clause 65.2 which uses the adjective 'wrong' as in 'wrong forecast'.

Clauses

18. Clauses should be as short as possible with no more than two sentences. They should cover only one subject.

Tenses

19. Use the present tense for all statements of what somebody must do or not do. It is seldom necessary to use another tense. 'If the sky has fallen down, the *Project Manager* decides what the *Contractor* will do' uses three tenses. 'If the sky falls down, the *Project Manager* decides what the *Contractor* does' uses only the present.

Capitals

20. Capital initials show that a term is defined in the contract. When drafting, test that a definition is right by putting it into the sentences where the defined term is used. These definitions are only abbreviations and must only be abbreviations. If there is anything to say about the defined term, it has to be in the clauses.

21. There are exceptions. *Project Manager, Supervisor, Employer* and *Contractor* have capitals but are not defined.

Particular words

22. 'May' in NEC means 'is allowed to' as in 'the *Supervisor* **may** instruct ......' Do not use it to mean that something might happen.

23. 'Any' can usually be deleted.

Multiple Alternatives

24. Either *a, b, c* or *d.* Bullet the alternatives if they are phrases of some length.

Chapter 4 ECC references to Works Information

The following table identifies where the *conditions of contract* refer to Works Information. Works Information should provide the information required by the contract and identify project specific requirements.

The references are in the order that they appear in the *conditions of contract* and cross referenced to the model form provided in Chapter 5.

ECC clause ref	Chapter 5	ECC clause description	Guidance on what should be included in the Works Information
11.2(2)	WI 405, 410	Completion is when the *Contractor* has • done all the work which the **Works Information** states he is to do by the Completion Date and • corrected notified Defects which would have prevented the *Employer* from using the *works* and Others from doing their work.	In order for the *Project Manager* to decide that Completion has occurred, the Works Information must state clearly and unambiguously what work is to be done before Completion.
11.2(5)		A Defect is • a part of the *works* which is not in accordance with the **Works Information** or • a part of the *works* designed by the *Contractor* which is not in accordance with the applicable law or the *Contractor*'s design which the *Project Manager* has accepted.	See Chapter 1.
11.2(7)		Equipment is items provided by the *Contractor* and used by him to Provide the Works and which the **Works Information** does not require him to include in the *works*.	
11.2 (19)		**Works Information** is information which either • specifies and describes the *works* or • states any constraints on how the *Contractor* Provides the Works and is either • in the documents which the Contract Data states it is in or • in an instruction given in accordance with this contract.	See Chapter 1.
20.1		The *Contractor* Provides the Works in accordance with the **Works Information**.	See Chapter 1.

ECC clause ref	Chapter 5	ECC clause description	Guidance on what should be included in the Works Information
21.1	WI 305	The *Contractor* designs the parts of the *works* which the **Works Information** states he is to design.	Define the parts of the *works* which the *Contractor* is to design. This can be done in a number of different ways. See Chapter 5 for further guidance.
21.2	WI 310	The *Contractor* submits the particulars of his design as the **Works Information** requires to the *Project Manager* for acceptance. A reason for not accepting the *Contractor*'s design is that it does not comply with either the **Works Information** or the applicable law. The *Contractor* does not proceed with the relevant work until the *Project Manager* has accepted his design.	State any procedures which the *Contractor* is to follow in carrying out his design and procedures for the submission of designs for acceptance by the *Project Manager* and Others.
22.1	WI 335	The *Employer* may use and copy the *Contractor*'s design for any purpose connected with construction, use, alteration or demolition of the *works* unless otherwise stated in the **Works Information** and for other purposes as stated in the **Works Information**.	State any restriction or additional purpose for which the *Employer* may wish to use and copy the *Contractor*'s design.
25.1	WI 905	The *Contractor* co-operates with Others in obtaining and providing information which they need in connection with the *works*. He co-operates with Others and shares the Working Areas with Others as stated in the **Works Information**.	Detail the activities of Others within the Working Areas.
25.2	WI 1005, 1010	The *Employer* and the *Contractor* provide services and other things as stated in the **Works Information**. Any cost incurred by the *Employer* as a result of the *Contractor* not providing the services and other things which he is to provide is assessed by the *Project Manager* and paid by the *Contractor*.	State the services and other things that are to be provided by the *Employer* and *Contractor*.
27.4	WI 1105	The *Contractor* acts in accordance with the health and safety requirements stated in the **Works Information**.	State any health and safety requirements for the project which the *Contractor* must follow.

ECC clause ref	Chapter 5	ECC clause description	Guidance on what should be included in the Works Information

31.2	WI 505	The *Contractor* shows on each programme which he submits for acceptance
		• the *starting date, access dates*, Key Dates and Completion Date,
		• planned Completion,
		• the order and timing of the operations which the *Contractor* plans to do in order to Provide the Works,
		• the order and timing of the work of the *Employer* and Others as last agreed with them by the *Contractor* or, if not so agreed, as stated in the **Works Information,**
		• the dates when the *Contractor* plans to meet each Condition stated for the Key Dates and to complete other work needed to allow the *Employer* and Others to do their work,
		• provisions for
		  • float,
		  • time risk allowances,
		  • health and safety requirements and
		  • the procedures set out in this contract,
		• the dates when, in order to Provide the Works in accordance with his programme, the *Contractor* will need
		  • access of a part of the Site if later than its *access date*,
		  • acceptances,
		  • Plant and Materials and other things to be provided by the *Employer* and
		  • information from Others,
		• for each operation a statement of how the *Contractor* plans to do the work identifying the principal Equipment and other resources which he plans to use and
		• other information which the **Works Information** requires the *Contractor* to show on a programme submitted for acceptance.
			State any additional information that the *Contractor* is to show on the programme. This may include dates for submission of designs and samples, dates for information or actions by the *Employer* and *Project Manager* and the timing of any test or inspection.
			
			Any requirements for the format of the programme should be stated, including the use of specific software and the requirement for hard or electronic copies. Any requirements for resource or financial data in the programme should also be stated.

31.3	WI 600	Within two weeks of the *Contractor* submitting a programme to him for acceptance, the *Project Manager* either accepts the programme or notifies the *Contractor* of his reasons for not accepting it. A reason for not accepting the programme is that • the *Contractor's* plans which it shows are not practicable, • it does not show the information which this contract requires,	Refer to clause 31.2 above.

ECC clause ref	Chapter 5	ECC clause description	Guidance on what should be included in the Works Information
31.3 (cont.)		• it does not represent the *Contractor*'s plans realistically or • it does not comply with the **Works Information**.	
35.2	WI 440	The *Employer* may use any part of the *works* before Completion has been certified. If he does so, he takes over a part of the *works* when he begins to use it except if the use is • for a reason stated in the **Works Information** or • to suit the *Contractor*'s method of working.	If the *Employer* requires to use any part of the *works* prior to Completion without taking it over, describe the part and set out the reason for it's use.
40.1	WI 705	The clauses in this clause only apply to tests and inspections required by the **Works Information** or the applicable law.	Detail the tests and inspections required, the results expected and which parties are involved in the test and inspection process.
40.2	WI 705	The *Contractor* and the *Employer* provide materials, facilities and samples for tests and inspections as stated in the **Works Information**.	State the materials, facilities and samples to be provided by the *Contractor* and the *Employer* for tests and inspections and the timing of these.
41.1	WI 705	The *Contractor* does not bring to the Working Areas those Plant and Materials which the **Works Information states are to be tested or inspected before delivery until the** *Supervisor* has notified the *Contractor* that they have passed the test or inspection.	State the Plant and Materials which are to be tested and inspected before delivery to the Working Areas, including details of tests or inspections.
45.1	WI 440	If the *Contractor* is given access in order to correct a notified Defect but he has not corrected it within its *defect correction period*, the *Project Manager* assesses the cost to the *Employer* of having the Defect corrected by other people and the *Contractor* pays this amount. The **Works Information** is treated as having been changed to accept the Defect.	

ECC clause ref	Chapter 5	ECC clause description	Guidance on what should be included in the Works Information
45.2	WI 440	If the *Contractor* is not given access in order to correct a notified Defect before the *defects date*, the *Project Manager* assesses the cost to the *Contractor* of correcting the Defect and the *Contractor* pays this amount. The **Works Information** is treated as having been changed to accept the Defect.	
60.1(5)	WI 905	The *Employer* or Others <ul><li>do not work within the times shown on the Accepted Programme,</li><li>do not work within the conditions stated in the **Works Information** or</li><li>Carry out work on the Site that is not stated in the **Works Information**.</li></ul>	Refer to clauses 25.1 and 25.2
60.1(16)	WI 705	The *Employer* does not provide materials, facilities and samples for tests and inspections as stated in the **Works Information**.	Refer to clause 40.2.
71.1	WI 1305	The *Supervisor* marks Equipment, Plant and Materials which are outside the Working Areas if <ul><li>this contract identifies them for payment and</li><li>the *Contractor* has prepared them for marking as the **Works Information** requires.</li></ul>	State the requirements for marking Equipment, Plant and Materials which are outside the Working Areas by the *Supervisor*, for payment and transfer of title to the *Employer*. The Works Information should state which items are to be prepared for marking and how this is to be done.
73.2	WI 1310	The *Contractor* has title to materials from excavation and demolition only as stated in the **Works Information**.	The Works Information should state which materials arising from excavations and demolitions the *Contractor* has title to.
C, D and E 11.2 (25)	WI 1405, 1410	Disallowed Cost is cost which the *Project Manager* decides <ul><li>is not justified by the *Contractor's* accounts and records,</li><li>should not have been paid to a Subcontractor in accordance with his contract,</li><li>was incurred only because the *Contractor* did not<ul><li>follow an acceptance or procurement procedure stated in the **Works Information** or</li><li>give an early warning which this contract required him to give</li></ul></li></ul>	State any acceptance or procurement, procedures to be followed by the *Contractor*. State any constraints on how the *Contractor* is to Provide the Works. This is relevant to Options C, D and E where payment to the *Contractor* is based upon Defined Cost.

ECC clause ref	Chapter 5	ECC clause description	Guidance on what should be included in the Works Information
C, D and E 11.2 (25) (cont.)		and the cost of • correcting Defects after Completion, • correcting Defects caused by the *Contractor* not complying with a constraint on how he is to Provide the Works stated in the **Works Information**, • Plant and Materials not used to Provide the Works (after allowing for reasonable wastage) unless resulting from a change to the **Works Information**, • resources not used to Provide the Works (after allowing for reasonable availability and utilisation) or not taken away from the Working Areas when the *Project Manager* requested and • preparation for and conduct of an adjudication or proceedings of the *tribunal*.	

F 11.2 (26)	WI 1405, 1410	Disallowed Cost is cost which the *Project Manager* decides
		
		• is not justified by the accounts and records provided by the *Contractor*,
		• should not have been paid to a Subcontractor in accordance with his contract,
		• was incurred only because the *Contractor* did not
		  • follow an acceptance or procurement procedure stated in the **Works Information** or
		  • give an early warning which this contract required him to give or
		• is a payment to a Subcontractor for
		  • work which the Contract Data states that the *Contractor* will do himself or
		  • the *Contractor*'s management.
			State any acceptance or procurement, procedures to be followed by the *Contractor*.
			
			This is relevant to Option F where payment to the *Contractor* is based upon Defined Cost.

C, D, E and F 52.2	WI 1505	The *Contractor* keeps • accounts of his payments of Defined Cost, • proof that the payments have been made, • communications about and assessments of compensation events for Subcontractors and • other records as stated in the **Works Information**.	Detail any other records to be kept by the *Contractor*.

ECC clause ref	Chapter 5	ECC clause description	Guidance on what should be included in the Works Information
X4.1	WI 1600	If a parent company owns the *Contractor*, the *Contractor* gives to the *Employer* a guarantee by the parent company of the *Contractor's* performance in the form set out in the **Works Information**. If the guarantee was not given by the Contract Date, it is given to the *Employer* within four weeks of the Contract Date.	Set out the form of parent company guarantee required.
X13.1	WI 1700	The *Contractor* gives the *Employer* a performance bond, provided by a bank or insurer which the *Project Manager* has accepted, for the amount stated in the Contract Data and in the form set out in the **Works Information**. A reason for not accepting the bank or insurer is that its commercial position is not strong enough to carry the bond. If the bond was not given by the Contract Date, it is given to the *Employer* within four weeks of the Contract Date.	Set out the form of performance bond required.
X14.2	WI 1800	The advanced payment is made either within four weeks of the Contract Date or, if an advanced payment bond is required, within four weeks of the later of • the Contract Date and • the date when the *Employer* receives the advanced payment bond. The advanced payment bond is issued by a bank or insurer which the *Project Manager* has accepted. A reason for not accepting the proposed bank or insurer is that its commercial position is not strong enough to carry the bond. The bond is for the amount of the advanced payment which the *Contractor* has not repaid and is in the form set out in the **Works Information**. Delay in making the advanced payment is a compensation event.	Set out the form of advanced payment bond required.

Chapter 5 *Employer*'s Works Information

There are many different ways to structure Works Information.

A straightforward Works Information structure is suggested in the NEC3 ECC Guidance Notes. This outline generally follows the sequence in which subjects arise within the *conditions of contract*. Many good Works Information documents have been compiled using this structure as a guide.

The example Works Information structure in this Chapter does not follow the order in which subjects appear in the *conditions of contract*. Instead it is an arrangement of topics for describing the *works*, flowing from general explanations and requirements to specific details. This structure also permits the voluminous documents (such as work specifications) to be included as appendices to make navigation and digestion of other Works Information sections easier.

Guidance is provided for each Works Information section. This includes a checklist of topics to help users prepare a complete statement of the *Employer*'s requirements. The checklist provides a list of topics which might need to be included – most project will not use all items.

Example Works Information Structure

The numbering used below is indicative.

Section	Works Information (*Employer*'s)
WI 100	Description of the *works*
WI 200	General constraints on how the *Contractor* Provides the Works
WI 300	*Contractor*'s design
WI 400	Completion
WI 500	Programme
WI 600	Quality assurance
WI 700	Tests and inspections
WI 800	Management of the *works*
WI 900	Working with the *Employer* and *Others*
WI 1000	Services and other things to be provided
WI 1100	Health and safety
WI 1200	Subcontracting
WI 1300	Title
WI 1400	Acceptance or procurement procedure (Options C, D, E and F)
WI 1500	Accounts and records (Options C, D, E and F)
WI 1600	Parent company guarantee (Option X4)
WI 1700	Performance bond (Option X13)
WI 1800	Advanced payment bond (Option X14)
WI 1900	Low performance damages (Option X17)
WI 2000	*Employer*'s work specifications and drawings

Guidance and Checklist

This relates to the example Works Information structure shown above. Guidance relating to each Works Information section is provided in the grey boxes. A checklist of optional topics is also provided.

WI 100 Description of the *works*

Provide a general description of the work to be carried out under the contract. Do not repeat the definition of the *works*.

The general description should be consistent with the description in Contract Data part one, and identify the outline scope of the works to be provided. A general description of the *Contractor*'s design responsibility may be included here. A detailed description is included in section WI 300.

The *Employer*'s overall objectives for the project may also be stated, so that the *Contractor* understands them and can work with the *Employer* to achieve them.

A description of works to be undertaken by the *Employer* or Others is in section WI 900.

Checklist	Explanation
WI 105 Description of the *works*	As above.
WI 110 Project objectives	Explain 'why' the project is being undertaken. Specific objectives may include outcomes on safety, quality, time and functionality.

WI 200 General constraints on how the *Contractor* Provides the Works

State any general constraints on how the *Contractor* Provides the Works, which are not covered by other Works Information sections.

If project objectives are included, state the requirements imposed on the *Contractor* in helping to achieve them.

Constraints may include the checklist topics listed below. Constraints are restrictions on how the *Contractor* Provides the Works, not issues related to cash flow, funding or other requirements which conflict with the *conditions of contract*.

Checklist	Explanation
WI 205 General constraints	Examples of constraints. • Use of the Site. • Access to the Site. • Deliveries. • Noise and vibrations. • Working hours, • Parking. • Use of cranes. • Use (or non-use) of explosives. • Restrictions on the use of hazardous materials. • Storage of fuel and chemicals. • Pollution, ecological or environmental impacts. • Archaeological requirements. • Interfaces between the *works* and existing things. • Occupied premises and users.

Checklist	Explanation
	• *Employer* specific policies and procedures. • Constraints imposed to meet the requirements of Others (for example funders).
WI 210 Confidentiality	Confidentiality and publicity restriction, and any acceptance procedures.
WI 215 Security and protection of the Site	Security requirements for the Site and protection of the public.
WI 220 Security and identification of people	Security, vetting and identification of people working on or visiting the Site. Requirements for people visiting Site.
WI 225 Protection of existing structures and services	Specific requirements for the protection of existing structures, services, mains, trees and other plants. Requirements for maintenance of existing services. Procedures for working on existing structures and services. Refer to Site Information for location of existing things to be protected or procedures for identifying them.
WI 230 Protection of the *works*	Specific requirements for the protection of the *works* against damage.
WI 235 Cleanliness of roads	Requirements agreed with authorities for protecting and cleaning of access roads to the Site.
WI 240 Traffic management	Requirements and procedures for management of traffic, road closures and public highways. Communication and information requirements.
WI 245 Condition survey	Condition surveys to be carried out by the *Contractor* and any associated reinstatement works.
WI 250 Consideration of Others	Restrictions on work to avoid disturbance to the general public or occupiers of adjacent premises.
WI 255 Industrial relations	Specific requirements for the *Contractor* to comply with any industrial relations policies.
WI 260 Control of site personnel	Requirements for control of people working on or visiting Site. Permits and licences (for example permits to work).
WI 265 Site cleanliness	Keeping the Site clean and tidy.
WI 270 Waste materials	Removal of waste and restrictions on the disposal of waste material. Requirements for recycling.
WI 275 Deleterious and hazardous materials	Restrictions on the use of deleterious and hazardous materials.

WI 300 *Contractor*'s design

Define the parts of the *works* which the *Contractor* is to design. The ECC is flexible in this respect. The responsibility for design can be described in a number of different ways, but in all cases, the part to be designed by the *Contractor* must be clearly identified. If the *Employer* carries out most of the design, a list of items designed by the *Contractor* may be stated. If the *Contractor* carries out most of the design, a list of items designed by the *Employer* may be stated.

State the procedures which the *Contractor* is to follow in carrying out his design and procedures for the submission of design for acceptance by the *Project Manager* and Others. Identify which parts of the design are required to be submitted to the *Project Manager* for acceptance.

Checklist	Explanation
WI 305 Design responsibility **ECC 21.1**	As above.
WI 310 Design submission procedures **ECC 21.2**	As above.
WI 315 Design approvals from Others **ECC 27.1**	State any requirement for design checks and approvals by Others.
WI 320 *Employer*'s requirements	Identify the *Employer*'s requirements for the parts of the *works* to be designed by the *Contractor*. Examples of this information are listed below. • Specifications, including reference to relevant standards. • Design standards and codes of practice. • Size and/or space limitations. • Loading and capacity requirements. • Operational performance requirements and design life. • Planning drawings and planning consents. • Energy consumption targets • Environmental standards • Sustainability requirements • Design quality evaluation criteria • *Employer*'s design reports • *Employer*'s standard design guidance.
WI 325 Design co-ordination	State what responsibility the *Contractor* has for co-ordination with Others in preparing his design and any responsibility for the coordination of design by Others.
WI 330 Requirements of Others	Explain the *Contractor*'s responsibility for obtaining and satisfying any necessary authority requirements (for example planning officials or government departments).

Checklist	Explanation
WI 335 Copyright/licence **ECC 22.1**	State any purpose for which the *Employer* may wish to use and copy the *Contractor*'s design if it is not as stated in clause 22.1.
WI 340 Access to information following Completion	• State the *Employer*'s requirements for access to information once the Defects Certificate is issued including timescale for the retention of information after Completion. Consider any need for computer software source code for example.

WI 400 Completion

Completion is when the *Contractor* has done all the work which the Works Information states he is to do by the Completion Date and corrected notified Defects which would have prevented the *Employer* from using the *works* and Others from doing their work. If the work which the Contractor is to do by the Completion Date is not stated in the Works Information, then Completion is when the *Contractor* has done all the work necessary for the *Employer* to use the *works* and for Others to do their work.

In order for the *Project Manager* to decide that Completion has occurred, the Works Information must state clearly and unambiguously what work is to be done before Completion.

Examples might include successful passing of stated key tests and provision of as-built documentation. Refer to section WI 700 for test and inspection requirements.

An alternative approach could be in the form of a statement of which part of the *works* can remain incomplete at the Completion Date.

It may also be useful to state the procedures to be adopted to ensure a smooth transition from construction to operation of the asset. This may also include procedures leading up to Completion and between Completion and the Defects Date.

Checklist	Explanation
WI 405 Completion definition **ECC 11.2(2)**	Work to be done by the Completion Date.
WI 410 Sectional Completion definition **ECC X5.1 (Option X5)**	As above for each Sectional Completion.
WI 415 Training	Training required for the *Employer* or Others and associated timescales.
WI 420 Final clean	Details of final clean, removal of temporary structures, materials, protection and tools.
WI 425 Security	Details of security arrangements and handover at Completion.
WI 430 Correcting Defects	Procedures for access for the correction of any Defects and process for liaison with the *Project Manager* and *Employer*.
WI 435 Pre-Completion arrangements	Requirements for preparing for take over.
WI 440 Take over **ECC 35.2**	Identify parts of the *works* that the *Employer* requires to use prior to Completion without taking it over. Details to include • location of parts of the *works* and • reasons for use. *Contractor*'s access provision during period of use.

WI 500 Programme

State any information additional to the requirements of ECC clause 31.2 that the *Contractor* is to include in the programme. This may include dates for submission of designs and samples, dates for information or actions by the *Employer* and *Project Manager*, and the timing of any test and inspection.

Any requirements for the format and content of the programme should be stated, including the use of specific software (if necessary) and the requirement for hard or electronic copies.

Checklist	Explanation
WI 505 Programme requirements **ECC 31.2**	As above.
WI 510 Programme arrangement	Any specific arrangement of the programme, including any requirement for the programme to be produced in levels (summary level to detail level).
WI 515 Methodology statement	Particular requirements for methodology statements, including any specific requirement for resource information.
WI 520 Work of the *Employer* and Others	The order and timing of the work of the *Employer* and Others to be included in the programme and information to be provided. Refer as necessary to sections WI 905 and WI 910.
WI 525 Information required	A schedule of information to be provided, who it is to be provided by, and the date by which it is to be provided.
WI 530 Revised programme	Any specific requirements for the submission of revised programmes, such as an explanation of changes.

WI 600 Quality management

Detail the requirements for quality control and management.

Checklist	Explanation
WI 605 Samples	State the materials and samples required including any procedures for submission and acceptance.
WI 610 Quality statement	Any requirement for a quality statement from the *Contractor*.
WI 615 Quality management system	Any requirements for a quality management system, including accreditations or legislative standards.

WI 700 Tests and inspection

Detail the tests and inspections required and which parties are involved in the test and inspection process. Tests and inspections may also be detailed within work specifications. Ensure consistency of drafting between this section and the contents of WI 2000.

Tests and inspections might be required for

- Samples of plant or materials provided by the *Contractor*.
- Samples of workmanship.
- Equipment, Plant and Materials outside the Working Areas before payment or delivery.
- Work in the Working Areas.
- Plant and Materials, and work prior to Completion (see WI 400).
- Plant and Materials, and work after take over but before the *defects date*.
- System tests.
- Computer software tests.
- Performance tests.

State the materials, facilities and samples to be provided by the *Contractor* and the *Employer* for tests and inspections, and the timing of these.

State the Plant and Materials which are to be tested and inspected before delivery to the Working Areas, including details of the test or inspection.

Any test or inspection of Equipment, Plant and Materials outside the Working Areas which have to be passed before marking by the *Supervisor* for payment should also be stated.

If secondary Option X17 Low performance damages applies, detail the relevant performance tests.

State any requirements for commissioning or performance tests in this section, in the same way that other tests and inspections are described.

Further guidance is in the NEC3 ECC Guidance Notes.

Checklist	Explanation
WI 705 Tests and inspections **ECC 40.1** **ECC 40.2** **ECC 41.1** **ECC 60.1(16)**	Consider the following checklist for test and inspection details. - Objective, procedure and standards to be used. - When they are to be done. - Where they are to be done.

Checklist	Explanation
	• Who does the tests, and who is in attendance. • Testing and inspection method. • The Equipment required and who provides it. • Access arrangements. • Information or instructions required to be provided. • Materials, facilities and samples to be provided. • Involvement of specialists. • Acceptable results and deviations. • Test environment. • Documents to be provided before and after the test. • Whether or not authorisation to proceed to the next stage of the work depends in the test results.
WI 710 Management of tests and inspections	Consider the requirement for a test and inspection schedule, containing all relevant information. State the procedures for submission and review.
WI 715 Covering up completed work	State timescales for the covering up of works which have been tested.
WI 720 *Supervisor*'s procedures for inspections and watching tests	State any inspection procedures required by the *Supervisor*.

 **nec**3

WI 800 Management of the *works*

The Contract Data identifies the *Employer*, *Project Manager*, *Supervisor* and *Contractor* and states what each is required to do. It is important, in using this section, not to contradict these obligations and duties. If any of their duties are delegated to Others, the extent of the delegation should be set out.

The ECC establishes a procedural framework based on good project management practice. It may be helpful to detail the communication procedures required to support this.

This may include a framework of regular meetings, attendees required and outputs. Explain how people will be involved in the management of the *works* and how communications are to be managed. Consider the use of a chart setting out the roles and responsibilities of the various parties involved.

State whether an internet based collaboration tool or other electronic communication system is to be used.

Checklist	Explanation
WI 805 Project team – Others	As above.
WI 810 Communications	State any communication procedures which the *Contractor* is required to follow. Consider the following. • Meetings, attendees and meeting records. • Reporting requirements (e.g. progress reports). • Information requirements. • Electronic systems and communications. • Use of standard forms and templates. • Terminology and abbreviations.

WI 900 Working with the *Employer* and Others

Detail the activities of Others within the Working Areas.

The *Contractor* is required to co-operate with Others in obtaining and providing information which they need in connection with the *works*. State any requirements that have been agreed with Others.

Checklist	Explanation
WI 905 Sharing the Working Areas with the *Employer* and Others **ECC 25.1** **ECC 60.1(5)**	Provide a list of activities to be undertaken, explaining the following. • What is being done. • Who is doing it. • When it is being done, and for how long. • Where it is being done. • How the *Contractor* is to co-operate and share the Working Areas.
WI 910 Co-operation	Identify known information requirements, for the *Contractor* to obtain from Others or provide to Others, and timing.
WI 915 Co-ordination	State how the *Contractor* is to liaise with the *Employer* and Others for the co-ordination of works and access.
WI 920 Authorities and utilities providers	Identify works to be carried out by authorities and utilities providers. State the responsibility for enquiry, management, procurement, provision of notices and payment.

WI 1000 Services and other things to be provided

State the services and other things that are to be provided by the *Employer* for use by the *Contractor*, and by the *Contractor* for use by the *Employer, Project Manager* or Others. Identify who they are provided for. It is not necessary to list things that the *Contractor* requires for his own use to Provide the Works.

State any requirements for quality and maintenance of services to be provided.

Checklist	Explanation
WI 1005 Services and other things for the use of the *Employer, Project Manager* or Others to be provided by the *Contractor* **ECC 25.2**	May include the following. • Accommodation. • Meeting rooms. • Storage facilities. • Catering. • Medical facilities and first aid. • Recreation. • Sanitation. • Security. • Copying. • Telephone, fax, radio or CCTV. • Computer equipment and services. • Sign boards and other signage. • Safety equipment and services. • Fences, screens and hoardings. • Postage. • Maintenance of access roads. • Temporary facilities. • Utilities, e.g. water and power. • Meter readings.
WI 1010 Services and other things to be provided by the *Employer* **ECC 25.2**	Same checklist as above. Consider the following also. • Access to the Site. • Space for accommodation. • Plant and Materials.

WI 1100 Health and safety

State any health and safety requirements for the project which the *Contractor* must follow, in addition to the requirements of law.

Refer to Chapter 4 for guidance on the inclusion of health and safety information in Works Information and Site Information.

Checklist	Explanation
WI 1105 Health and safety requirements **ECC 27.4**	Details of any additional health and safety requirements for the project, all which may include the following. • *Employer*'s safety requirements. • Reporting requirements. • Safety management, supervision and qualifications. • Management of Subcontractors. • Drug and alcohol policy. • Site induction procedures.
WI 1110 Method statements	Detail the operations for which the *Contractor* is required to submit method statements and risk assessments to the *Project Manager* for acceptance.
WI 1115 Legal requirements	If any health and safety duties are required by law, state who will perform them.
WI 1120 Inspections	State any requirement for review and inspection of *Contractor*'s health and safety procedures by the *Project Manager*.

WI 1200 Subcontracting

The *Contractor* may subcontract work using an NEC contract. Any restrictions on the *Contractor* subcontracting work need to be set out.

The ECC does not provide for nomination of subcontractors, for the reasons explained in the NEC3 ECC Guidance Notes. Alternatives to achieve similar objectives are

• make the *Contractor* responsible for all work; he may then subcontract parts and the *Project Manager* retains some control over the identity of the Subcontractors using ECC clause 26 or
• provide for separate contracts, with the *Project Manager* managing the time and physical interfaces between them.

Checklist	Explanation
WI 1205 Restrictions or requirements for subcontracting	State any restrictions and additional procedures which the *Contractor* must follow.
WI 1210 Acceptance procedures **ECC 26.3** **ECC 11.2(25) – Options C, D and E** **ECC 11.2(26) – Option F**	State any specific submission and acceptance procedures for proposed subcontracts not based upon an NEC contract. The basic requirement for submission and acceptance is dealt with at clause 26.3.

WI 1300 Title

State the requirements for marking Equipment, Plant and Materials which are outside the Working Areas by the *Supervisor*, for payment and transfer of title to the *Employer*. The Works Information should state which items are to be prepared for marking, and how this is to be done. Identify any tests which must be passed before items are accepted for marking.

The Works Information should state which materials arising from excavations and demolitions the *Contractor* has title to.

Checklist	Explanation
WI 1305 Marking **ECC 71.1**	As above.
WI 1310 Materials from excavation and demolition **ECC 73.2**	Decide the title of materials from excavation and demolition. State whether the *Employer* wishes to salvage any such materials, and if so where they are to be delivered to or collected from, and by whom.

WI 1400 Acceptance or procurement procedure (Options C, D, E and F)

State any acceptance or procurement procedures which apply in addition to the constraints set out within section WI 1210. This is relevant to Options C, D, E and F where payment to the *Contractor* is based upon Defined Cost. The definition of Disallowed Cost refers to acceptance and procurement procedures stated in the Works Information.

WI 1500 Accounts and records (Options C, D, E and F)

Detail any records to be kept by the *Contractor*, in addition to those listed in clause 52.2.

Checklist	Explanation
WI 1505 Additional Records **ECC 52.2 (Options C, D, E and F)**	List the additional records to be kept by the *Contractor*. This may include the following. • Timesheets and Site allocations sheets. • Equipment records. • Forecasts of the total Defined Cost. • Specific procurement and cost reports. Define the format and presentation of records to be kept.

WI 1600 Parent company guarantee (Option X4)

Include the form of parent company guarantee required.

WI 1700 Performance bond (Option X13)

Include the form of performance bond required.

WI 1800 Advanced payment bond (Option X14)

Include the form of advanced payment bond required.

WI 1900 Low performance damages (Option X17)

State the detailed requirements, performance standards and required tests, relating to any performance levels stated in the Contract Data for Option X17, if not already stated in section WI 705.

WI 2000 *Employer*'s work specifications and drawings

Include here the detailed work specifications and drawings which describe the *works*. A contents list may be provided or the documents themselves may be included or both.

Guidance for including work specifications is in Chapter 3.

Checklist	Explanation
WI 2005 *Employer*'s work specification	Contents list or documents or both.
WI 2010 Drawings	Contents list or documents or both.

Chapter 6 Works Information provided by the *Contractor* for his plan

The purpose of this section of Works Information is to include the *Contractor*'s proposals and design details for *works* which he is to design. This may include Plant and Materials, workmanship specifications, details and drawings. A contents list may be provided or the documents themselves may be included, or both.

Note that, where the particulars of the *Contractor*'s design are to be submitted for acceptance during the contract under clause 21.2, these submissions do not form part of the Works Information. The only person that can change the Works Information is the Project Manager under the various clauses in the contract. However, if the Contractor does not construct the works in accordance with the accepted design, that will be a Defect under clause 11.2(5).

Works Information prepared by the *Employer* is separated from any Works Information prepared by the *Contractor* relating to his design. The *Contractor* cannot prepare his Works Information until the *Employer*'s Works Information has been prepared.

There should be no ambiguity or inconsistency between the *Contractor*'s Works Information and the *Employer*'s Works Information.

Care should be taken where the *Contractor* has offered an alternative proposal to the *Employer*'s Works Information. If the *Employer* decides to accept the alternative proposal, the *Employer*'s Works Information must be changed. There are two options for the *Employer* in this situation

- if the E*mployer* assumes design responsibility for the alternative proposal, then the *Employer*'s Works Information is changed to incorporate it. It is not included within the *Contractor*'s Works Information, or
- if the *Contractor* retains design responsibility for the alternative proposal, then the *Employer*'s Works Information is changed to remove any redundant or conflicting content, and the alternative proposal is included in the *Contractor*'s Works Information.

Note that the *Employer*'s Works Information is treated as having priority over the *Contractor*'s Works Information under clause 60.1(1).

This page was amended in November 2015 and replaces previous versions.